FAMILYLIFE® presents

STEPPING UP™

A CALL TO COURAGEOUS MANHOOD

BASED ON THE BOOK BY DENNIS RAINEY

VIDEO EVENT

WRITTEN BY
TIM GRISSOM AND JOHN MAJORS

FamilyLife Publishing®
Little Rock, Arkansas

STEPPING UP: A CALL TO COURAGEOUS MANHOOD
VIDEO EVENT MANUAL

FamilyLife Publishing®
5800 Ranch Drive
Little Rock, Arkansas 72223
1-800-FL-TODAY • FamilyLife.com
FLTI, d/b/a FamilyLife®, is a ministry of Campus Crusade for Christ International®

Unless otherwise noted, Scripture quotations are from The Holy Bible, English Standard Version® (ESV®), copyright © 2001 by Crossway, a publishing ministry of Good News Publishers. Used by permission. All rights reserved.

Scripture quotations marked (NASB) are taken from the New American Standard Bible®. Copyright © 1960, 1962, 1963, 1968, 1971, 1972, 1973, 1975, 1977, 1995 by The Lockman Foundation. Used by permission. (www.Lockman.org)

Scripture quotations marked (NIV) are taken from the Holy Bible, NEW INTERNATIONAL VERSION®. Copyright © 1973, 1978, 1984, 2011 by Biblica, Inc. All rights reserved worldwide. Used by permission.

LEGO® is a registered trademark of the LEGO Group.

FamilyLife, FamilyLife Publishing, and Stepping Up are trademarks of FLTI.

Video event manual written by Tim Grissom and John Majors

ISBN: 978-1-60200-570-9

Design: Brand Navigation, LLC
Photography: iStockphoto and BigStock

Printed in China

16 15 14 13 12   1 2 3 4 5

FAMILYLIFE®
Help for today. Hope for tomorrow.

Boys take, Men give.

Boys criticize, Men create.

Boys complain, Men solve.

Boys consume, Men serve.

Boys pout, Men endure.

—JOHN BRYSON

CONTENTS

YOUR STEPPING UP EVENT MANUAL

Today's event will consist of four sessions, each one a blend of watching the video, responding to some questions on your own, and discussing a few points with the men around you. Your host will give you instructions for each session; you'll also want to watch for on-screen prompts that will direct you to notes, exercises, and other features in your manual.

At various times throughout the day, you will be encouraged to look inward through the **GETTING YOUR BEARINGS** exercises. There are eight of these, most will take three minutes or less to complete, a few will take longer. You will work through these on your own.

There are also three times designated for group discussion, labeled **CIRCLE UP** in your manual. These provide opportunities for you to hear what other men are learning, as well as a chance to verbalize your thoughts and ideas.

As a way of connecting all that you'll encounter today, the manual will also guide you through the process of developing a personal **STEPPING UP CREED**. This creed will highlight your own response to the four sessions, serving as a reminder of any life adjustments or affirmations you hope to make.

There are other related pieces scattered throughout your manual, including sidebars, statistics, and articles. You probably won't have time to look at many of these during today's event, but we encourage you to read them at a later time.

FOREWORD

ABOUT TODAY, ABOUT LIFE

Welcome to the Stepping Up video event for men. I'm glad you're joining us.

In my own journey through manhood, I've discovered three progressive truths:

I have to be intentional.
I must rely on God.
I need other men.

I have to be intentional. There's just too much turbulence out there to rely on autopilot. I can't afford to drift from one day to the next, one decision to the next, one assignment to the next and expect to be successful. I will fail, or at the very least under-deliver—as a husband, dad, and friend—if I'm always in reactive mode. If my life is to have a purpose, then I must live it purposefully.

I must rely on God. Though second on my list, this is the most important truth. I must never treat God as an add-on. With Him at the center, at the core, I have constant access to His grace, mercy, help, and wisdom. Without Him, I have nothing and I am nothing.

I need other men. This is really an extension of relying on God. I need the encouragement, training, and yes even the correction that God sends my way through other men. This is the great truth of Proverbs 27:17, "Iron sharpens iron, and one man sharpens another." Other men sharpen me; they make me a better man.

Everything you see and hear at today's Stepping Up event is wrapped around these three truths. May it be a life-shaping day for you. And as you go through this day, I encourage you to begin thinking about five other men you could challenge to join you in going through our ten-session Stepping Up video series.

Go deeper together, and keep on stepping up!

Dennis Rainey,
president and CEO of FamilyLife

1

SURVEYING THE TERRAIN

DEFINING MANHOOD

It may seem cliché to relate the journey of manhood to climbing a mountain, but the parallels are many. Climbing requires perseverance, training, and dependence on others. It requires a varied skill set that changes based on climate and terrain. It is filled with setbacks, and the challenge is immense. A seasoned climber will tell you that the journey up a tall peak is epic in its toll on his life and resources, but also in its reward for the accomplishment.

The only way to reach the top is to keep moving up. Sure, sometimes you have to intentionally backtrack, or spend the night in camp to acclimate, but you can only reach the top by putting one foot in front of the other.

And that's what men do. They keep stepping up, even when everything around them is screaming, "Stop! This hurts! This isn't fun anymore!" They take one more step. They keep the goal in sight and press toward it.

Just as challenging as moving in the midst of misery is making sure you are *on* the mountain. When does a boy know he's transitioned from the adolescent foothills and set his feet firmly on Mount Manhood?

WILD VOICES

A boy becomes a man when he

reaches a
certain age

hits puberty

drives a car

stops living
with his
parents

joins the
military

gains
responsibility

experiences
sex for the
first time

takes care
of someone

puts others
before
himself

loses
something
important

understands
what family
really means

doesn't rely on
others to do
what he should
do for himself

WHEN DOES A BOY BECOME A MAN?

It is an age-old question: When does a boy become a man? Most modern cultures lack clear points of entry. Sure, there is the occasional remnant of transition, such as the bar mitzvah or Eagle Scout ceremony, but even these events are in decline and lack the clarity a boy needs.

The South Pacific island nation of Vanuatu has a people group that makes transition into manhood quite clear to their boys by practicing the ancient tradition of land diving. Prior to the ritual, the village elders build a 100-foot-tall rickety tower. Then, to prove their manhood to the tribesmen below, the bravest young men climb to the top, tie vines to their ankles, and jump head first into a pile of soft dirt. It's an ancient version of bungee jumping, without any bungee. If the chief engineer designed everything properly, the divers' shoulders should just barely graze the supple soil. If not, then the villagers are spared the trouble of digging a grave.

What does this practice have to do with manhood? It's a bit of a moving target, as boys are not allowed to participate until after they've been circumcised at eight (years, not days). Once a boy feels he's ready for the challenge, he climbs to a lower platform (only the manliest jump from the top) and prepares to jump. His mother holds up one of his favorite childhood items (toy spear, loin cloth, or King Kong plush toy) and waits for the jump. If he survives, she tosses the adolescent relic in the trash; it is no longer needed because he's now a man.

Interesting practice, but probably not one to propose to your family. The point is that pursuing ceremonies and rituals to help boys with this transition is a worthy and rewarding endeavor. Robert Lewis has been encouraging men for years to establish rituals in their families. Check out his book *Raising a Modern-Day Knight* for stories of what he did with his boys and ideas for you to try.

Instructions for Land Diving

- Prepare the soil.
- Select the proper banana leaf for fashioning your athletic support device.
- Check your vines for the proper length.
- Check them again.
- Climb to the top.
- Make sure your will is written and accessible by your loved ones.
- Say a quick prayer and leap out as far as you can.
- Try to avoid undermining your manhood by screaming like a twelve-year-old girl at a Justin Bieber concert.
- Just before slamming into the ground, tuck your chin to your chest so that only your shoulders lightly graze the ground.
- If everything goes well, dust off your forehead and walk away proudly.
- Don't try this at home. Seriously, don't.

getting your bearings

Take three minutes to work through the following questions on your own.

1. **When did you first see yourself as a man? Check all that apply.**

   After I

   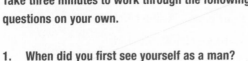

   - ☑ Started my first job
   - ☑ Had kids
   - ☑ Married
   - ☑ Got my driver's license
   - ☐ Attended a bar mitzvah

   - ☑ Turned eighteen
   - ☐ Graduated from high school
   - ☐ Joined the military
   - ☐ I'm not sure
   - ☐ Other:_____

2. **How would you describe your transition from adolescence to manhood? Check all that apply.**

   - ☑ Slow
   - ☐ Painful
   - ☐ Haphazard
   - ☐ Too fast
   - ☐ Awesome

   - ☐ Unintentional
   - ☐ Deliberate
   - ☐ Exciting
   - ☐ Out of Control
   - ☐ Other: _____

3. Take a moment to write down a few thoughts about what did help or would have helped make this transition better; (for example, "I wish my dad would have talked more about it"). The point of this exercise is not to condemn anyone for what they didn't do, but to help you be more proactive with your children as the opportunity presents itself.

WHAT DOES IT MEAN TO BE A MAN?

Be watchful, stand firm in the faith, act like men, be strong. Let all that you do be done in love. —1 CORINTHIANS 16:13–14

WHAT DOES "ACT LIKE MEN" MEAN? IT MEANS DON'T ACT LIKE A WOMAN.

Then the LORD God said, "It is not good that the man should be alone; I will make him a helper fit for him. —GENESIS 2:18

James MacDonald

Don't act like a woman means

1. DON'T FOLLOW, LEAD.

Leadership is "the ability to communicate a compelling state of affairs in a way that engenders followership."

He [the serpent] said to the woman, "Did God actually say, 'You shall not eat of any tree in the garden'?" —GENESIS 3:1

2. DON'T BE THE WEAKER VESSEL.

Likewise, husbands, live with your wives in an understanding way, showing honor to the woman as the weaker vessel, since they are heirs with you of the grace of life, so that your prayers may not be hindered. —1 PETER 3:7

3. LOSE THE DRAMA!

Be stable.

Proverbs says . . .

- A fool speaks his mind. (18:2)
- A fool is wise in his own eyes. (12:15)
- The vexation of a fool is known at once. (12:16)
- A fool belittles his neighbor but lacks sense. (11:12)

WHAT DOES "ACT LIKE MEN" MEAN? IT MEANS DON'T ACT LIKE AN ANIMAL.

WHAT MAKES A MAN

There is a lot of confusion in the culture about manhood these days. Peruse the popular men's magazines, and the formula becomes painfully predictable. The shining example set forth for all to follow is typically the latest tough-guy actor or high-profile athlete. The advertisements then provide the map for modeling your life after them: wear the right watch, drive the right car, sip a suitable beverage, don some groovy glasses (lenses optional), and of utmost importance, be arrayed in apt attire, preferably a slim-cut suit (how often does one wear suits?). Polish off the package with a pair of shoes (no socks) that cost more than your first car.

If you do all of these things, along with eating hundreds of salads a day and mastering the fine art of making sushi, all while working out four to seven hours a day and launching a venture capital firm, then maybe, just maybe, you'll land the right girl, and then you'll be a real man.

Yet in the midst of these guidelines and practical articles like "How to Shave Your Scrotum" (huh?), there is a chasm of content on the key components of authentic manhood. Things like character development, investment in the next generation, leaving a lasting legacy, faithfulness, integrity, and fidelity all go unnoticed.

The pull of the magazine ideal of manhood tugs at the hearts of men every day, but if you want to learn to leave a lasting legacy, the data screams to look elsewhere.

DEFINING MANHOOD

According to Voddie Baucham, the culture measures manhood by the three B's.

BILLFOLD
BALL FIELD
BEDROOM

Robert Lewis offers a four-point definition of manhood that he developed while working with men in his church:

1. A man rejects passivity.
2. A man accepts responsibility (see chart on next page).
3. A man leads courageously.
4. A man expects a greater reward.

. . . looking to Jesus, the founder and perfecter of our faith, who for the joy that was set before him endured the cross, despising the shame, and is seated at the right hand of the throne of God.

—HEBREWS 12:2

" WHEN I WAS A CHILD, I SPOKE LIKE A CHILD, I THOUGHT LIKE A CHILD, I REASONED LIKE A CHILD. WHEN I BECAME A MAN, I GAVE UP CHILDISH WAYS. "

—1 CORINTHIANS 13:11

The Bible highlights three areas where a man is given responsibility:

(1) A **will** to obey, (2) a **woman** to love, and (3) a **work** to do.

The Bible also highlights two men as being representative of all of mankind: Adam and Christ. It is helpful to note the way both of them responded to their responsibilities. One accepted and the other rejected the plan God set before him.

For as by the one man's disobedience [Adam's] the many were made sinners, so by the one man's obedience [Christ's] the many will be made righteous. —ROMANS 5:19

For a man . . . is the image and glory of God. —1 CORINTHIANS 11:7

	Adam	Christ
	The first man to appear on the scene. He was breathed to life by God himself. Adam means *"from the ground."* Or *"red."* His sin *"cast a shadow"* on all of humanity and reduced manhood.	Called the second Adam (1 CORINTHIANS 15:47) because of the way He redeems, or *"shines light"* on humanity.
1. A will to obey	God's will: *" . . . of the tree of the knowledge of good and evil you shall not eat."* (GENESIS 2:17) Adam's response: *. . . and he ate.* (GENESIS 3:6)	God's will: *"I lay down my life that I may take it up again. . . . This charge I have received from my Father."* (JOHN 10:17-18) Christ's response: *He said "It is finished," and he bowed his head and gave up his spirit.* (JOHN 19:30)
2. A woman to love	*And the rib that the LORD God had taken from the man he made into a woman and brought her to the man.* (GENESIS 2:22)	*Christ loved the church and gave himself up for her.* (EPHESIANS 5:25)
3. A work to do	*"Be fruitful and multiply and fill the earth and subdue it, and have dominion over the fish of the sea and over the birds of the heavens and over every living thing that moves on the earth."* (GENESIS 1:28)	*Christ reconciled us to himself and gave us the ministry of reconciliation.* (2 CORINTHIANS 5:18)

getting your bearings

Take fifteen minutes to process the following
questions on your own.

1.   Based on what you just heard, what would you say are
     some of the most important aspects of manhood?

     To Be a Le

2.   Looking back at 1 Corinthians 13:11 (page 12), what are some things boys need
     to put away?

3.   Conversely, if there are things a boy needs to "put away" to become a man,
     what kind of things does a man need to intentionally "take up"?

     Pray

4.   Thinking of your journey as a man, what is one area of manhood where you need
     to give attention more than any other? (It might help to look back to your notes
     from Robert Lewis's teaching and James MacDonald's segment on manhood.)

5.   Why has this particular area been a struggle for you?

6.   What do you need to do differently to put away things that have hindered your
     ability to grow in this area?

PART 2

THERE WAS A DAY WHEN YOU WOULD MOVE FROM BOY TO MAN, AND THERE WAS SOME INDICATION OF WHEN THAT WAS. NOW WE DON'T KNOW . . . AND THE RESULT IS THAT YOU'VE GOT A BUNCH OF BIOLOGICAL ADULTS BUT EMOTIONAL CHILDREN . . . BOYS WHO CAN SHAVE. "

—MARK DRISCOLL

THE LURE OF ADOLESCENCE

What is the lure of adolescence? Why are men easily drawn back into boyhood, shirking responsibility and living only for themselves?

Think back to the average twenty-five-year-old man of 1950. Most likely he had served in one of the most brutal wars civilization had ever experienced. When he came home, he married, landed a job—

probably a trade of some sort—and had kids. Before long he bought a house and likely lived there well into his retirement years, if not the rest of his life.

Compare this to the average twenty-five-year-old man today. More than likely he has done some college. If he graduated, he might have landed a job, but may be exploring other options, such as graduate school or world travel. He probably has a girlfriend, but he's not ready to commit to anything long term. He more than likely has a dog that he loves dearly. Ask him about his goals for life and they probably center around making money and experiencing the world, though he's not sure yet what his calling is. More than likely he has moved back in with his parents (if he ever left) or is at least keeping his old bedroom as an option.

This is clearly a caricature of the two ages. Not that we want to return to 1950, with the world on the cusp of war in Korea and the spread of global communism. There was certainly a cultural undercurrent flowing away from traditional biblical values.

But is the state of manhood better now than then? No doubt the men of today seem to have more fun finding themselves and exploring their options, but has it made for a better society, a better place for women and children?

> **THE REASON WHY WE HAVE THIRTY-, FORTY-, FIFTY-YEAR-OLD ADOLESCENTS . . . [IS] THE BREAKDOWN OF THE FAMILY OVER THE LAST THIRTY-FIVE TO FORTY YEARS. WITH THE RISE OF THE DIVORCE RATE AND THE INCREASED FEMINIZATION OF MEN, WHAT WE'RE FINDING IS A RETICENCE OF MEN TO STEP UP AND STEP OUT.**
>
> —CRAWFORD LORITTS

HOW TO GET UNSTUCK

IF YOU ARE FEELING STUCK IN ADOLESCENCE:

- Begin by believing that God has created you in His image for a specific purpose, and has a great vision for your life.

- Know that He has great love for you and cares deeply about you.

- God does not want to see you fail in your pursuit of life in Him (John 10:10).

- Identify what has you stuck.

- Recognize that time is fleeting. You must develop a sense of urgency about getting unstuck (Ephesians 5:16).

- Choose one thing you are passionate about and identify one action you can take this week. Meet with a guy you admire who can give you advice and encouragement in this area.

IF YOU KNOW SOMEONE WHO IS STUCK:

- Begin by encouraging him, letting him know he's unconditionally loved, that he's not alone, and he's not the first person in the world to be stuck.

- Drive him to clarify his future. Help him to objectify where he needs to be, and keep asking him, "So what are you going to do?"

- Remind him that taking responsibility will strengthen, not destroy him.

- Let him know you will be there to help him get over the hump.

CLIMBING MOUNT EVEREST

The Tetons have much to offer, but when it comes to climbing, there is no higher peak than Everest. If you're thinking of giving it a whirl, here are some facts to whet your appetite:

- Edmund Hillary was first to the top, on May 29, 1953.
- His journey took three months, 400 people, and 10,000 pounds of baggage.[1]
- Since then, 3,142 have ascended the summit (as of 2010).[2]
- Over 200 have died attempting the climb.[3]
- Average cost to climb is $60,000.[4]
- Allow two months to make the trek.

Other helpful things to know:

- If you make it, you can now text your grandmother to celebrate, since cell phone service was installed in 2010.

- If Everest seems too easy for someone of your extreme manliness, set your sights on Mr. Apa Sherpa, who has climbed it a record twenty-one times.[5]

- And since nothing is manlier than a shortcut, Frenchman Didier Delsalle was the first to fly to the top via helicopter in May 2005.[6]

Take thirty minutes to discuss the following questions
in your group.

1. How does our culture define manhood?

2. How does this compare to what Robert Lewis and James
    MacDonald shared?

3. Why is there so much confusion about manhood and what it
    means to be a man?

CIRCLE UP

4. In your opinion, when does a boy become a man?

5. Who do you know that embodies real manhood?

6. If you are willing to share, what is the one area of manhood where
    you feel you need to grow in the coming year? (Refer to question 4
    in Getting Your Bearings on page 14.)

7. On your own take 5–10 minutes to complete the "Wrapping it Up"
    exercise on the following page.

WRAPPING IT UP

Write down one thing you need to do a better job of as a man.

Now write it in a way to fit into the following statement:

I will be a man who _____ .

For instance, if you hope to grow in your ability to be responsible, write, "I will be a man who can be depended on no matter what."

Here are some other examples:

I will be a man who . . .

CHARACTER:	does what's right all the time.
INTEGRITY:	is the same in public as he is in private.
PERSEVERANCE:	does the hard thing when he feels like giving up.
FAMILY:	sacrifices for the sake of those he loves.
PRIORITIES:	keeps life and work in a proper balance.
FAITH:	knows that life is best experienced as a faithful follower of Christ.
TEACHABILITY:	knows when to admit he's wrong.
REPENTANCE:	can ask for forgiveness.

It's important that your statement fit this sentence because of the bigger purpose for this day. By the end of the day, we hope to help you develop a personalized Stepping Up Creed, one that fits who you are and addresses the main themes of each session. You will be filling in the following four statements:

I will be a man who

I will display courage by

I will pursue godliness by

I will make a difference by

You can see the final creed on page 77.

Once you have written your statement for this session, transfer it to the creed on page 77, and then take a break to prepare for session two.

2

SCALING THE SUMMIT

LIVING COURAGEOUSLY

At many points in life a man's courage will be put to the test. Sometimes his intimidator might be a well-armed and angry enemy, but at other times it might be a skinny, pimply faced boy who's starting to ask questions about girls. And at other times that man might need courage to face off against his own appetites that are pushing him toward decisions that could kill his character and destroy his family.

There is a difference between being courageous and never being afraid. Courage causes a man to look at life realistically and to accept responsibility. Never being afraid is . . . fantasy. Courageous men trust God and serve others. Courageous men are dependable and humble.

Are you living courageously?

> **REMAIN AT YOUR POST AND DO YOUR DUTY—FOR THE GLORY OF GOD AND HIS KINGDOM.**
>
> —CHARLES "CHUCK" COLSON

Chuck Colson (1931–2012) was known for two primary reasons: (1) his role in the Watergate scandal of 1972 that sent him to prison and forced the resignation of President Richard M. Nixon, and (2) his founding of Prison Fellowship, an evangelical outreach to prisoners and their families.

> **THE MEN OF 9/11 WERE MEN WHO DID WHAT MEN ARE SUPPOSED TO DO IN THE FACE OF DANGER. THEY WERE MEN WHO WENT FORWARD INSTEAD OF PULLING BACK.**
>
> —DENNIS RAINEY

According to the U.S. Fire Administration, an estimated 81,070 firefighter injuries occur each year in the U.S.[1] On average, 100 firefighters are killed each year in the line of duty.[2]

"I feel 'meant' to do this."

"Not that I can change the world, but I can change this scene. I can do something about this, right now."

"You're still nervous, but you do it anyway."

"Something that you learn from day one when you come to the firehouse is: you have to step up. You have to take responsibility. Become selfless."

Hero or Celebrity?

A hero serves. A celebrity takes. A hero avoids the limelight. A celebrity can't get enough of it. A hero grieves when he can't save every soul. A celebrity renegotiates his contract when a colleague gets a pay raise.

We need more heroes.

WILD VOICES

What does courage mean to you?

Jumping into the unknown. I really didn't have a clue what I was embarking on at the time.

Oftentimes we do things courageously that we don't really think are courageous at the time we do them.

Think about the dangers and think about the rewards and decide if you can handle the risk.

I've never really had a courageous moment.

Courage . . . you have to have it every day in the little moments and the little choices. They add up.

Courage is waking up every morning with the will to live.

getting your bearings

Take three minutes to answer the following.

1. How do you define courage?

2. Who is the most courageous person you have known?

My Wife

3. Why do you think of this person as courageous?

HOW TO KILL A GIANT

We can learn many things from the life of David, but the clear message coming out of his encounter with Goliath is about courage. Here are five observations about courage from 1 Samuel 17.

 1. GOD'S REPUTATION MATTERS MOST.

David was approximately seventeen years old at the time of his bloody encounter with Goliath. Even at that age he was an up-and-comer, already getting face time with King Saul and members of his court, and privately anointed to be Saul's successor. Still, David's courage was neither a display of youthful arrogance nor the strutting of an opportunist. In his mind, none of what would happen that day in the Valley of Elah was about him. He cared only that the reputation of God was under attack. For that, David would put two things on the line that most men would never part with: his safety and his reputation.

David approached the fight with no human assurance that he would survive and virtually no support from his comrades. In fact, they accused him of being a fool and a show-off (cowards often slander the courageous). Of course, he was neither. In choosing to live and serve for the pleasure of God, David had already taken into account the possibility of dying for Him. Fighting God's enemies was something David *had* to do.

 2. BIGGER AND LOUDER DOES NOT MEAN STRONGER.

Goliath had the advantage in every measurable category. He was bigger than David. He was more experienced than David. His weapons were larger, heavier, and custom-made. He had forty days' worth of momentum on his side. And he was setting all the terms and conditions of the fight. Time was running out for the army of Israel. There were only two possible outcomes: (a) surrender, or (b) massacre.

That is, until the wiry shepherd boy's faith kicked in and activated his bravery. Suddenly it was Goliath who was in big trouble (pun intended). By faith David knew that it wasn't he Goliath would fight, but God.

Many battles are lost because they're never fought, and they're never fought because men tend to believe only what their eyes see and their ears hear. The habitual neglect of God in everyday life will undermine a man's faith in the threatening moments when he needs faith most. David didn't suddenly conclude that God was enough while Goliath was flashing his sword and spear; his courage was rooted in a well-cultivated friendship with God. David didn't survey the scene, then factor in God's existence and abilities; his thoughts began with God.

Tomorrow might be a tough day for you or your family. You should start preparing for it today. How? By "growing in your knowing" of God.

Goliath stood approximately 9′9″ tall. His coat of mail (body armor) weighed 125 pounds!

3. COURAGE ISN'T A BADGE TO FLASH, BUT A SERVICE TO OFFER.

You've got to admire David's humble attitude and feel a little ashamed that it was unusual even in the company of God's people. When he was brought into the king's tent, David said, "Let no man's heart fail because of [Goliath]. Your servant will go and fight with this Philistine" (1 Samuel 17:32).

David could have bad-mouthed his cowardly cohorts and thereby called attention to his own bravery. But that would have been showmanship, not courage. And David was no showman. His motivation was to serve and protect. It didn't even occur to him that this could be his chance to slip from the obscurity of sheep watching into the limelight of national heroism. He said, "Your *servant* will go and fight." Servants *do* because others can't or won't. They are motivated by need, prepared by faith, and satisfied with God's approval. Nothing more, nothing less. There may be times in a man's life when he has to defend himself, but most of his battles will be fought on behalf of others.

4. BRAVERY CANNOT BE BORROWED.

The part of the story where David tries out Saul's armor is often told with humor because it is assumed that the pieces were all too big and heavy for David (vv. 38–40). And while that might have been the case, it is really just speculation. The actual reason David gave for refusing Saul's armor was simply that it was unfamiliar to him; he reasoned that in the intensity of the fight it would have slowed him down and made him vulnerable.

David chose to face Goliath with the same outfit and weaponry he had used as a shepherd to kill lions and bears. These were things he knew and trusted. To his warrior's heart, it made no sense to face a life-or-death situation armed only with what another man said would be good enough.

It is helpful to be with men who live by courageous faith, but do not get lulled into thinking that you can survive on borrowed bravery. The time will come when you will have to face challenges and responsibilities all on your own, no tag-teaming. Are you ready?

5. COURAGE DISPLAYED IS COURAGE INSPIRED.

While we cannot borrow someone else's bravery, we can be inspired by another to act courageously. This is exactly what happened with the army of Israel after they watched David kill Goliath: "The men of Israel and Judah rose with a shout and pursued the Philistines" (v. 52). These men whose fear had confined them to camp for forty days suddenly went on the offensive, not only chasing their enemy but soundly defeating them. What had changed? They had seen courage in action and they were inspired.

Sometimes it takes only one man who is willing to trust God with everything and do the right thing to revive courage in the hearts of his brothers.

Be that man.

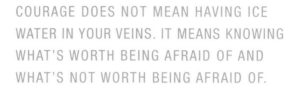

COURAGE MEANS DOING THE RIGHT THING IN EVERY CIRCUMSTANCE REGARDLESS OF THE COST.

—STU WEBER

COURAGE DOES NOT MEAN HAVING ICE WATER IN YOUR VEINS. IT MEANS KNOWING WHAT'S WORTH BEING AFRAID OF AND WHAT'S NOT WORTH BEING AFRAID OF.

—BILL BENNETT

Courage doesn't call us to just do *something*, it calls us to do the *right* thing.

MOST OF US ARE NOT GOING TO STARE DEATH IN THE FACE AND SMILE AT IT. MOST OF US ARE GOING TO RAISE OUR CHILDREN, LOVE OUR WIVES, AND FAITHFULLY SERVE THE BODY OF CHRIST. / COURAGE COULD ALSO BE PULLING INTO YOUR DRIVEWAY AND, EVEN THOUGH YOU'VE JUST WORKED EIGHT-, TEN-, TWELVE-HOUR DAYS, KNOWING YOUR JOB IS NOT OVER YET.

—MATT CHANDLER

"My dad was great . . . not because he did any earth-shattering thing, but because every day of his life he showed up."

What will your sons and daughters say about you?

—Crawford Loritts

COURAGE IS A RADICAL OBEDIENCE IN THE FACE OF WHAT SCARES YOU TO DEATH. IT'S NOT PULLING BACK, IT'S PRESSING INTO YOUR FEARS. IT'S NOT DENYING YOUR FEARS, BUT IT'S SEEING WHAT NEEDS TO BE ADVANCED— WHAT NEEDS TO BE ACCOMPLISHED—AS GREATER THAN YOUR PERSONAL COMFORT.

—CRAWFORD LORITTS

"

BEING COURAGEOUS DOESN'T MEAN NOT BEING AFRAID. IT'S THE OPPOSITE, THAT WHEN YOU ARE AFRAID COURAGE IS COUNTED ON THE MOST AND NEEDED THE MOST. / COURAGE IS A WILLINGNESS TO DO WHAT YOU HAVE TO DO WHEN YOU DON'T WANT TO DO IT.

—VODDIE BAUCHAM

COURAGE IS A BY-PRODUCT OF THE FEAR OF THE LORD. THE FEAR OF THE LORD JUST SAYS THAT IF THIS IS WHAT GOD SAYS, IF THIS IS WHAT GOD WANTS, IF THIS IS WHAT GOD DEMANDS, THEN THAT'S WHAT I'M GOING TO DO. YES, I MIGHT GET CRITICIZED. YES, I MIGHT GET FIRED. YES, I MIGHT FAIL. YES, I MIGHT BE REJECTED. YES, I MIGHT DIE. BUT IF THAT'S WHAT THE LORD HAS ASKED ME TO DO, THAT'S WHAT I'M GOING TO DO BECAUSE THE LORD LOVES ME AND I LOVE THE LORD . . . IT'S THAT GODWARD THEOLOGICAL TRAJECTORY OF LIFE THAT SAYS IT'S NOT ABOUT ME, IT'S ABOUT HIM . . . YOU HAVE TO REDEFINE SUCCESS AS BEING OBEDIENT.

—MARK DRISCOLL

ONE OF THE BIGGEST CHALLENGES WE FACE AS MEN IS THE COURAGE TO CONFRONT OUR OWN SINFUL APATHY. / IT TAKES COURAGE TO STAND UP TO OUR OWN DESIRES.

— JOSHUA HARRIS

COURAGE IS BEING SCARED OUT OF YOUR MIND AND SADDLING UP ANYWAY.

— JOHN WAYNE

"

getting your bearings

Take fifteen minutes to consider the personal implications of what you just viewed by working through the following exercise.

1. Many of the men in this session admitted that there are things that make them afraid or cause them anxiety. In fact, courage wouldn't really be needed if fear and intimidation didn't exist. So, be honest, what are some areas in your life where you need to display courage (in your marriage, with your children, with friends, initiating changes in your personal life, etc.)?

2. As you consider these areas, what fears do you have to confront in order to fulfill your responsibilities and do your duty as a man?

3. Don't let the fact that you have fears overwhelm
   you. These present you with great opportunity to
   trust God for courage. But you must resolve in your
   heart, before God, that you will not give in to these fears
   and that you will stop letting them influence the way you live. Think of the one fear
   that causes you the greatest concern, the one you most need to overcome at this
   time in your life. Are you ready to go to battle against it? If so, complete the
   following statement by writing that fear on the blank line.

I will not retreat from __*fear*__.

Now, turn your recognition of fear into a statement of action that you intend to take to overcome it.

I will display courage by __*Pary*__.

Finally, transfer this statement to your Stepping Up Creed on page 77.

PART 2

COURAGEOUS MENTORS

> I'VE BEEN HUGELY IMPACTED BY KEY MENTORING RELATIONSHIPS. SOME PURISTS WOULD LOVE TO RUN IN AND SAY, "JUST FOLLOW JESUS. JESUS IS YOUR MENTOR." AND THAT IS TRUE, BUT PAUL SAID TO THE CORINTHIANS, "FOLLOW ME AS I FOLLOW CHRIST." A KEY VERSE FOR ME IN THE WHOLE MENTORING RELATIONSHIP HAS BEEN 2 TIMOTHY 2:2, WHERE PAUL SAID TO TIMOTHY, "AND WHAT YOU HAVE HEARD FROM ME IN THE PRESENCE OF MANY WITNESSES ENTRUST TO FAITHFUL MEN WHO WILL BE ABLE TO TEACH OTHERS ALSO." . . . EVERYBODY NEEDS TO FIGURE OUT WHERE THEY ARE IN THAT CHAIN AND BE THE LINK THAT GOD HAS CALLED THEM TO BE. / EVERY TIME SATAN TAKES SOMEBODY DOWN IN SCRIPTURE—HE'S THE ROARING LION LOOKING FOR WHOM TO DEVOUR—THAT'S A ONE-PERSON-AT-A-TIME SPORT. HE DOESN'T TAKE DOWN A HERD OF MEN; HE TAKES THEM DOWN ONE AT A TIME. WE STRONGLY ENCOURAGE OUR MEN TO GET TOGETHER . . . IT IS A LIFELINE TO ACCOUNTABILITY, MUTUAL DISCLOSURE OF SIN, EXPERIENCE OF CONFESSION AND FORGIVENESS TOGETHER, SUPPORT TO DO WHAT'S RIGHT. I JUST DON'T KNOW HOW YOU COULD LIVE AS A CHRISTIAN MAN IN THIS WORLD TODAY AND TRY TO DO IT ALONE. "

—JAMES MACDONALD

> **"** I'M MOST SHARPENED BY MEN WHO ARE STRONG IN AREAS THAT I AM WEAK. IF YOU WANT TO GROW, FIND MEN WHO PROVOKE YOU. **"**
>
> —JOSHUA HARRIS

> **"** SOMETIMES MENTORING TAKES PLACE IN A MOMENT. SOMETIMES IT TAKES PLACE OVER A LIFETIME. **"**
>
> —STU WEBER

> **"** WE NEED MEN IN OUR LIVES WHO SEE US AS CLOSELY AS POSSIBLE, THE WAY WE REALLY ARE. THERE ARE MEN AROUND US WHO, IF WE SHARE LIFE WITH THEM, GET TO SEE ASPECTS OF OUR LIFE AND OF OUR CHARACTER THAT ARE BLIND SPOTS FOR US. AND WE NEED THAT IN OUR LIVES. WE ALSO NEED TO KNOW THAT THOSE MEN ARE THERE AND THAT WHEN WE CALL UPON THEM THEY WILL BE HONEST WITH US, AND THEY WILL FORCE US TO BE HONEST AS WELL. **"**
>
> —VODDIE BAUCHAM

> **"** MORE THAN YOU NEED *A* GUY, YOU NEED *GUYS*. I THINK IT'S WAY TOO MUCH TO PUT ON ONE MAN THE CALL TO MENTOR YOU IN ALL THESE DIFFERENT AREAS OF LIFE. FOR ME THAT NEEDS TO BE A GROUP OF MEN. **"**
>
> —MATT CHANDLER

BE A MENTOR

COMMON EXCUSES

1. I don't feel qualified.

    Remember, some of the greatest lessons you have to pass on to others are through your errors.

2. I don't know how.

    You can receive online training through FamilyLife.com/ementoring.

3. I don't know who to ask.

4. I don't know how to ask.

WHERE DO YOU START?

Take an inventory of your life:

What are the life lessons I have learned?

What have been your key failures
(that now give you a voice to address
these issues)?

What are your skills and gifts?

WHAT I TEACH OTHER MEN

The truth about who God is

The danger of pride and a self-focused heart

How to handle adversity

The importance of honoring their parents

> **GOD MADE YOU TO MENTOR!
> LOOK UP. LOOK AROUND. THE BROKEN
> PEOPLE YOU SEE THAT HAVE NEEDS
> MAY BE READY-MADE FOR YOU TO
> BEGIN A MENTORING RELATIONSHIP.**
>
> —DENNIS RAINEY

> **WITH UPRIGHT HEART
> HE SHEPHERDED THEM
> AND GUIDED THEM WITH
> HIS SKILLFUL HAND.**
>
> —PSALM 78:72

What My Mentors Have Taught Me[3]
Dennis Rainey

Here are just a few of the things I've learned
from mentors who've come alongside me
through the years:

- The best measure of what a man can do
  is what a man has done.

- Making bad decisions helps you learn to
  make good decisions.

- Once the facts are clear, usually the right
  decision jumps out at you.

- Communication is not what is said but
  what is heard.

- Every man needs margin in his calendar
  for the unexpected at work and at home.

- No amount of success at work will
  compensate for failure at home.

- Debt is dangerous.

- Lifelong male friendships are challenging,
  but every man needs a friend who can
  speak truth into his life.

- A man needs to be accountable to
  another man.

- Praying with his wife is the most powerful
  thing a husband can do every day.

- Every man is leaving a legacy, so why not
  be intentional about the legacy you leave?

- A life lived without God, the Scriptures,
  and complete, daily surrender to Jesus
  Christ is a wasted life.

In this session we discussed courageous living and mentoring. Take thirty minutes to discuss the session in your group, using the following questions as a guide.

LIVING COURAGEOUSLY

1. Do you think there is a difference between being courageous and never being afraid? If so, what is the difference?

2. Look back to the descriptions of courage on pages 32–33. Choose one that you find especially meaningful or helpful and explain why you chose it.

COURAGEOUS MENTORS

3. Do you agree that it takes courage to be a mentor? Explain your answer.

4.	Describe at least two or three life lessons you have learned or are learning from other men.

5.	If you are mentoring someone right now, or have done so in the past, describe your approach to mentoring.

6.	Dennis Rainey talked about taking an inventory of our lives to discover what our skills and gifts are, as well as the failures and mistakes of our past that now give us a way of helping others. What does your life inventory reveal that can be key to equipping you as a mentor?

ARE YOU READY TO STEP UP AND INTO THEIR LIVES?

They are out there and they need you—boys without dads, young men under bad influence, and grown men aching for real friendship. Some of these guys are in your life already, by God's design.

See page 75 for a suggestion about how you can help them.

Scan this code to learn about Stepping Up apps.

3

STRENGTHENING YOUR HEART

BUILDING *a* LIFE *of* FAITH

Some challenges are relatively easy to deal with—a slight schedule adjustment here, a delayed purchase there, more time doing this, less time doing that. But other challenges are complicated, presenting drastic and long-term consequences. Even eternal ones.

A man's faith is the core of his life. No goal, priority, or cause, regardless of the intensity you bring to it, can override the effects that faith has on the way you live. Unless and until your faith is set where it needs to be, in Christ, you are more vulnerable than you know. And once set, it must not be neglected.

44

Top Five Regrets

Bronnie Ware, an author and musician from Australia, also cares for patients who are in their final weeks of life. She wrote a blog post about the most common regrets her patients expressed to her. Her blog post eventually became the theme of her book, *The Top Five Regrets of the Dying: A Life Transformed by the Dearly Departing.* The top five regrets she discovered are as follows: [1]

1. I wish I'd had the courage to live a life true to myself, not the life others expected of me.

2. I wish I hadn't worked so hard.

3. I wish I'd had the courage to express my feelings.

4. I wish I had stayed in touch with my friends.

5. I wish I had let myself be happier.

Michael Vick played quarterback at Virginia Tech, where he placed third in the Heisman Trophy balloting after his freshman season. He left after his sophomore year to enter the NFL draft. He was selected by the Atlanta Falcons, where he played for six seasons. In 2007 he pleaded guilty to felony charges for his involvement in an interstate dog-fighting ring. After serving twenty-one months in prison, he was released. Vick later signed with the Philadelphia Eagles and was reinstated to play in the NFL in 2009.

THE CLEANSING POWER OF SHAME

Have you ever been ashamed? Not just embarrassed, but ashamed. So remorseful of something you'd said or done that you could barely lift your head?

Good. Shame can help you become the man God wants you to be.

Listen to what God had to say about his people in the book of Jeremiah:

> *Were they ashamed when they committed abomination?*
> *No, they were not at all ashamed;*
> *they did not know how to blush.* (6 : 1 5 A)

God was calling His people to forsake their wicked ways and return to him. But, sadly, God knew they had grown so attached to their sin that they were no longer ashamed of it. Their minds were closed and their hearts were calloused. It no longer occurred to them that sin was disgraceful. Their sin—their cozy, coddling love affair with sin—had robbed them of God's power. And soon they would suffer the consequences.

Don't disregard this warning as a thing of the past. Sin is as damaging as ever. And sin with no shame can still be catastrophic. Christian men invite their own downfall when they go soft on sin.

So be glad when your sin shames you; this is a strong indication that God is at work in your heart. Let that shame drive you to return to God, to repent of your sin, and to be restored in your soul to love Him first and most. And then, don't just seek to be a man with no shame. Set your sights higher by striving to be a man who has no reason to be ashamed.

getting your bearings

1. What are your greatest regrets?
   Think both in terms of things you have done
   and things you have not done.

2. Dennis Rainey said, "When there are cracks in the spiritual foundation of a
   man's life, that man will approach the finish line with a lot of regrets." How
   would you define the current condition of your personal spiritual foundation?

   ☑ It's solid, holding, and getting stronger.
   ☑ An occasional crack shows, but I repair them as soon as I see them.
   ☑ There are some hairline cracks that need attention now.
   ☑ I never really gave my spiritual foundation much thought.
   ☑ My spiritual foundation is unreliable.

3. Now that you've inspected your foundation, is there some need you should
   address? If so, what is it?

THE COURAGE TO SURRENDER

The most important decision a man will make is to give his life to Jesus Christ. In other words, the most courageous thing a man will ever do is surrender, that is, surrender himself to God.

Life apart from God is less than futile and locked on a collision course with tragedy. Consider these scriptures:

> *There is a way that seems right to a man, but its end is the way to death.*
>
> —PROVERBS 14:12

> *The wages of sin is death.* —ROMANS 6:23

Sin separates us from God, and there's nothing we can do to close the gap. Though we may try to earn God's approval by working hard to become better people, we must understand that the problem of sin runs so deep that our best behavior cannot zero it out. We need a Savior, a Rescuer.

Jesus Christ is our Rescuer! Through Him God has provided salvation. Jesus lived a holy life in perfect obedience to God and willingly died on a cross to pay the penalty for our sin. Then He proved that He is more powerful than sin or death by rising from the dead.

> *"I am the way, and the truth, and the life. No one comes to the Father except through me."* —JOHN 14:6

> *God shows his love for us in that while we were still sinners, Christ died for us.* —ROMANS 5:8

> *The wages of sin is death, but the free gift of God is eternal life in Christ Jesus our Lord.* —ROMANS 6:23

To be rescued we must give up every effort to save ourselves and put complete trust in Him whom God sent. This is surrender, not to an enemy but to a deliverer. Jesus has provided the way—the one and only way—to establish a relationship with God.

Do you have the courage to surrender your life to God? Nothing you've done or will do in life matters more than this decision. You can turn to Christ, surrender your life to Him, and begin the adventure of allowing Jesus Christ to transform your life today.

If you are interested in learning more, talk to your Stepping Up host or one of the men in your group. They will be glad to help you.

❝ WRETCHED MAN THAT I AM! WHO WILL DELIVER ME FROM THIS BODY OF DEATH? THANKS BE TO GOD THROUGH JESUS CHRIST OUR LORD! ❞

—ROMANS 7:24–25A

MANLY REMINDERS FROM CRAWFORD LORITTS

- Don't get lazy about holiness in your life.

- What you think is hidden says a lot more than you intend.

- We need to revisit a sense of urgency about our lives. Character cannot be casual.

MAKING PROMISES

We're all aware of the pain that a broken promise can bring, especially to a child. And while we hear much about the importance of keeping our promises, have you ever thought about whether a promise should have been made in the first place? Here are a few questions to consider before making a promise to your son or daughter.

1. WHY ARE YOU MAKING THIS PROMISE?

There are many good reasons for making a promise to your child, including lifting his spirit, giving her something to look forward to, rewarding obedience, and many others. But there are also bad motivations, including appeasing your own guilty conscience. If there is a breakdown in the relationship with your child because of something you've done wrong, admit it. Apologize. Show courage by being honest and humble. A child can see through the manipulation of promise-making by guilt. And more important, so can God.

2. IF THERE ARE CONDITIONS, DOES YOUR CHILD UNDERSTAND THEM?

Because there are so many things beyond your control, some promises have to be conditional. If you have a job that often requires you to be called in without warning over the weekend, be careful about promising your family a lake outing on Saturday. You can certainly tell them you want to, and that you're even planning on it, but they need to understand that plans can change. The challenge with this is that when an adult says *maybe*, a child tends to hear *definitely*. That's why it is important to communicate over and over what your intent is, but also to remind them that you can't control everything. And while none of us likes to see our children disappointed, it is a life lesson they must learn. Of course an obvious antidote is to keep every promise you can and to find a way to make up for those you can't.

3. ARE YOU REALISTICALLY COUNTING THE COST?

Our words can easily get us into trouble, especially when we speak off the cuff. Promises are sometimes made in a hurry and, if we're honest, in an attempt to get someone's approval. Be very careful about making promises without first taking the time to consider whether you can deliver.

4. ARE YOU CURRENT ON YOUR TRUSTWORTHINESS?

The real power of a promise isn't as much in the promise as it is in the one who makes it. Your children may *enjoy* the lake, but they *love* you. It's you they really want. This is a two-edged sword. A promise kept is proof to your children that you love them and want to do things with them. But if you break a promise, it's you they're disappointed in. The lake didn't let them down, you did. Keep your promises and you'll keep your children's trust in you alive.

Remember, some promises should never be made in the first place. But once a promise is made, it should be kept. Trust and dependability communicate love.

MANLY REMINDERS FROM BILL BENNETT

- Don't be just a game-day player. Practice.

- If you only do 80 percent, you're embarrassed all the time.

- The best way to teach a person responsibility is to hold them responsible.

NO LOITERING

Business owners often post this sign as a way of saying, "If you don't have a reason to be here, move on." It's meant as a warning, but what's the real harm in loitering? Doing nothing is better than causing trouble or committing a crime, right?

Not necessarily. The problem with loitering, let's call it idleness, is that it generally moves a person toward bad choices and destructive behavior. Remember what happened to King David?

> *In the spring of the year, the time when kings go out to battle, David sent Joab, and his servants with him, and all Israel. And they ravaged the Ammonites and besieged Rabbah. But David remained at Jerusalem. It happened, late one afternoon, when David arose from his couch and was walking on the roof of the king's house, that he saw from the roof a woman bathing; and the woman was very beautiful.*
>
> —2 SAMUEL 11:1–2

Before this sordid part of David's life was over, he had committed adultery and murder. And it all began because he was loitering in Jerusalem when he should have been on duty with his army.

Proverbs 18:9 goes so far as to say, "Whoever is slack in his work is a brother to him who destroys," making clear the connection between idleness and destructiveness. This points to a growing problem in our culture: too many of our young men are loitering. They're wandering aimlessly through life, not understanding the power of daily choices or the long-term consequences of inertness. And we're not just talking about getting a job and showing up on time. We're talking about wasted days that become wasted years and men living low. We're talking about men God wants to use who disqualify themselves, not through some great evil deed, but through doing nothing. Nothing at all. Nothing every day.

These young men are playing when they could be preparing. For what, who knows? But this much is certain, the man who can be depended on, the man who will meet the challenges life will bring, and the man who can help lead and protect others, won't be the man who loitered throughout his youth. He will be the man who prepared. The man who learned through the daily decisions of responsible living, who fulfilled his assignments to the best of his abilities, and who accepted help when he needed it and offered it when he had it to give.

getting your bearings

Take fifteen minutes to work through the
following exercise.

1. If you know Christ, what are some of the ways that knowing Him helps you step
    up to real manhood?

2. Crawford Loritts urged men not to get lazy about holiness in their lives. The
    pursuit of God requires consistency and intentionality. How would you describe
    the level of effort you are currently giving to your own spiritual development?
    Check the description that best fits, or write your own.

    - ☑ I am doing all that I know to do, and I am growing spiritually.
    - ☑ I have given more effort in the past, but I think I'm doing okay.
    - ☐ I haven't given it much thought.
    - ☐ I could be doing more, but I can't seem to find the motivation.
    - ☐ Other: _____

3. Can you identify an area of your life, or perhaps a few, that seems to hinder your
    spiritual growth the most? What is it?

4. What step are you willing to take right away that will throttle up your spiritual
    growth? Answer by completing the following statement:

    I will pursue godliness by _____.

    Once you are satisfied with your answer, transfer it to your Stepping Up Creed
    on page 77.

PART 2

> " WE ARE ALL JUST ONE SLIPPERY STEP AWAY
> FROM A FALL. ONE FOOLISH CHOICE CAN WIPE OUT
> YEARS OF INTEGRITY. "

—DENNIS RAINEY

At a 2003 meeting of the American Academy of Matrimonial Lawyers, two thirds of the 350 divorce lawyers who attended said the Internet played a significant role in the divorces that year, with excessive interest in online porn contributing to more than half such cases.[2]

In 2006, there were 68 million daily pornographic requests on Internet search engines—25 percent of total search engine requests.[3]

STEPS TO SEXUAL FREEDOM[4]

WHEN A MAN CONFIDES THAT HE IS STRUGGLING WITH PORN, HERE ARE THREE IMMEDIATE ASSIGNMENTS THAT CAN HELP:

1. In the next twenty-four hours, get alone with God. Confess this as sin. Tell Him that you agree with Him that looking on a woman to lust is wrong and offensive to Him.

2. In the next seven days, meet with a man you respect and trust and confess your sin to him. Ask him to hold you accountable and pray for you in this area.

3. In the next two weeks, tell your wife. Seek her forgiveness for this sin against her. Tell her that you need her to be your ally and to pray for you and encourage you to live a godly life.

ALSO, CALL HIS ATTENTION TO THREE THINGS:

1. Most men turn to porn when they are hungry, lonely, angry, or tired. This is when they are most vulnerable. This is why I urge them to have an offensive strategy in place, not just a defensive strategy. They need to be prepared to fight and win.

2. Every woman you ogle online, or in real life for that matter, is some man's daughter. Undoubtedly, she is sad and lonely and has been robbed of her dignity. How would you respond if other men looked at pictures of your daughter?

3. Finally, look to the gospel. This is ultimately a heart issue, not a behavior issue. You need what the Puritan Thomas Chalmers called "the expulsive power of a new affection." You need to cultivate a heart for the things of God. When tempted to look at porn, turn instead to the Scriptures, to prayer, and to fellowship with others.

BE STRONG!

For the sake of Christ, then, I am content with weaknesses, insults, hardships, persecutions, and calamities. For when I am weak, then I am strong.

—2 Corinthians 12:10

If your right eye causes you to sin, tear it out and throw it away. For it is better that you lose one of your members than that your whole body be thrown into hell. And if your right hand causes you to sin, cut it off and throw it away. For it is better that you lose one of your members than that your whole body go into hell.

—Matthew 5:29–30

But put on the Lord Jesus Christ, and make no provision for the flesh, to gratify its desires.

—Romans 13:14

> **MAKE DECISIONS IN A MOMENT OF STRENGTH THAT WILL SUPPORT YOU IN A MOMENT OF WEAKNESS.**
>
> —JAMES MACDONALD

Note: Because the nature of this discussion could be personal and revealing, you may prefer to discuss these questions with just one other man, or a few, rather than in a larger group. We do encourage you to discuss them with someone rather than just working through them on your own. Men need each other, especially in matters as important as moral purity.

1. Have you ever taken a drastic step to battle sin in your life (for example: dealing with anger, overcoming substance abuse, avoiding the temptation of pornography)? Describe the struggle you were having and the action you took to try to overcome it.

CIRCLE UP

2. What area of your personal life is of greatest concern to you right now? Why is it a concern?

3. If you could get help from another man, or group of men, in this area of your life, what would you ask them to do?

4. What steps are you presently taking to protect yourself and your family from the dangers of sexual immorality?

5. Reflect on James MacDonald's statement: "Make decisions in a moment of strength that will support you in a moment of weakness."

    ● What commitments are you willing to seriously consider making?

    ● What commitments are you prepared to make right here and now?

6. Pray for one another in your group. Ask God to give each man an urgent desire to live a life of moral uprightness.

SHOWING THE WAY

STEPPING UP *to* LEAD

> ❝ WE NEED HEROES. WE NEED GROWN-UPS . . .
> IT'S TIME TO GET YOUR HANDS DIRTY. IT'S TIME
> TO ANSWER THE CALL OF MANHOOD. IT'S TIME
> TO WEAR THE PANTS! ❞
>
> FROM AN ADVERTISEMENT FOR DOCKERS JEANS

Speaking of pants, you can tell a lot about a guy by the pants he wears:

Pants type	What it says about you
SKINNY JEANS	Not claustrophobic, knows how to make a great latte, and has nothing to hide.
CARGO PANTS	Ready for anything. Can provide a knife, ink pen, notebook, bottle opener, or screw driver at all times. Eagle Scout.
KHAKIS	Emotionally prepared for either a business meeting or a stroll on the beach.
DRESS SLACKS	401k is fully vested. Golf clubs are too.
COWBOY JEANS	Likes a good rodeo now and then. Would choose John Deere over BMW any day. American made is the only way.
LEATHER	Rides a Harley, or is a lifetime member of the *Grease* fan club.
BIKER SHORTS	Likes exercise and shaving, a lot. Also doesn't mind complete strangers knowing his circumcision status.
TIGHTS	Ballet dancer, amateur Shakespearean actor, or completely out of touch.

Of course, pants don't tell the entire tale about a man.
There's much more to leadership than pants.

WILD VOICES

What makes a great leader?

looks out for
his people

sets an
example

takes
charge

stands by
their word

has
convictions

not afraid to
stand up for
what is true

stands firm
during trials

sets their own
pride aside
for others

does the
right thing

ESSENTIAL LEADERSHIP

History is replete with leaders of all types. There are the conquering military types like Napoleon, Alexander the Great, and Robert E. Lee. The force of their personalities combined with their military brilliance inspired nations to follow along for the conquest. Then there are the orators, the great motivational leaders like Winston Churchill, Ronald Reagan, and William Wallace—men who stirred throngs with their words and ideas. There are also the unconventional leaders, those who took indirect paths, such as Martin Luther King Jr., Gandhi, and Joan of Arc, who launched revolutions from the bottom up, creating momentum through leading by example and living out their convictions.

When it comes to leadership, there are plenty of people to model, but it's also important to have your own list of qualities you see as essential, things that set apart a good leader from a bad one.

getting your bearings

What are the top qualities of an effective leader?
Take three minutes to answer the following questions.

1. Which of the following leadership characteristics are most important to you?
    Check all that apply.

    ☑ Respectful   ☐ Creates opportunities
    ☐ Challenging   for people to grow
    ☐ Energetic   ☑ Fun to work with
    ☑ Able to push people   ☑ Smart
      further than they   ☐ Good communicator
      would go on their own   ☑ High character
    ☐ Gracious   ☐ Displays integrity
    ☐ Not a micro-manager   ☐ Gives clear direction
    ☑ Helps people think ahead   ☑ Works well with a team
    ☐ _____   ☐ _____

2. Of the above qualities you checked, list the three you consider most important.

    Respectful

    Fun to Work with   *Work well with a team*

3. On a scale of 1 (high) to 5 (low), rate yourself in each of the three areas.

    5 work well with a team

4. How do you think others would rate you? (If you dare, take time tonight to ask
    your wife or a close friend to rate you in each of these areas.)

LEADING YOUR WIFE

Mark Driscoll

What does it mean for a husband to lead his wife? Ephesians 5:23 says, "The husband is the head of the wife even as Christ is the head of the church." Some men, after hearing they are the head of their wives, have understood this to mean that a man can order his wife around and treat her like a slave. Let's be very clear here: any man who does this has misread, misunderstood, and misapplied these verses in a grossly inappropriate way. No man who reads all of Ephesians 5:23–30 could honestly come to such a conclusion.

Men who rip these verses out of context and use them as bullying devices to abuse and belittle women are completely clueless about the meaning of the Bible and even the most basic commands like "Love your neighbor as yourself." It's even fair to ask whether they truly know Christ.

In these verses, something profound is actually happening. Paul called a man to lead as Christ leads the church, sacrificially, treating his wife as his own body, which he should "nourish and cherish" and "cleanse her with the washing of the water of the word." The language here is very gentle and caring. No man could truly fulfill his responsibility as the leader of his home without learning to lovingly sacrifice his own life for the sake of his wife.

LEADERSHIP AND VISION

James MacDonald says that when it comes to leading your family, the vision must be that "There is no success apart from loyalty and commitment to Jesus Christ."

The two big tools a leader uses to bring about this vision are CLARITY and URGENCY.

> "Without it [a biblical vision of success] we lose no matter what we win, and with it we win no matter what we lose."
>
> —James MacDonald

SEEING VISION

How can you be clear about your vision and make sure it matters? Carve out an hour alone sometime in the next week and ask yourself the following questions:

1. Do I really believe this vision to be true (referring to James MacDonald's teaching on the video)?

2. If not, why?

3. If so, what do I need to be doing in my home to make this vision true?

4. What do I need to deconstruct or stop doing to make this vision true?

5. How does my relationship with my children need to change?

6. How does my relationship with my wife need to change?

7. What is one thing I can do to begin setting this vision in motion?

Getting Started

- Meet with an older man to talk about how he went about setting vision.

- Attend a conference.

- Read a book on the topic.

- Take a planning retreat away with my wife.

- Begin a regular date with my kids to talk about life.

- Write a draft of a plan by _____ (set a deadline) and ask _____ (name of respected friend) to hold me accountable to it.

getting your bearings

The emphasis of this chapter has been on leadership in the context of a family. But men also need to be thinking about leading in all areas of their lives. As Josh Harris said, "Men are called to lead."

1. Consider the needs in your immediate family and in other key relationships. Here are some questions to help you think. Choose two or three to answer.

   ● What needs in your family concern you most? *Talk*

   ● If you are married, in what ways does your relationship with your wife need to be stronger? *Love + Talk*

   ● If you have children, how would you describe your relationship with each one? What are some areas in which they need to grow (spiritually, emotionally, character, life skills, and so on)?

   ● How would you evaluate your relationship with your parents? What needs to improve?

   ● What situations are you concerned about at work? In your church? In your community? *None*

2. Now, look back over the list and see if there are any relationships you avoided because they seemed too painful or difficult to deal with. God is calling you to come alongside someone (or yourself) and help them accomplish something they cannot or will not on their own. If you took the easy way, write down the name and need of the person you skipped here:

3. Of these needs, which should be the highest priority in your life right now? Which should get the most time and attention? If you're not sure, take a moment to pray and seek direction from God on this (James 1:5), then write it below. (You might be tempted to select the easiest need on your list. But remember, leadership means doing the right thing, the hard thing, even when you don't want to.)

4. Leadership doesn't mean you will solve every problem, but it does mean that you are willing to take initiative to improve them. Write down some actions you can take to address one or two of the situations you identified.

5. Once you have one leadership need identified, try to write it in a way that makes sense in this sentence:

   I will make a difference by _____.

   Examples:

   providing for my family.

   getting myself clean from _____ -Or- helping _____
   get clean from _____.

   making my broken relationship with _____ right.

Once you have this statement written, transfer it to your Stepping Up Creed on page 77.

Before moving on, try to identify one action you can take to meet this need. For instance, if you wrote, "help my sister avoid divorce," think of an action you can take this week, like "Invite my sister and her husband to a marriage conference." Write that action point here:

PART 2

" LEADING A FAMILY TAKES PERSEVERANCE. IT'S A LONG, SLOW PROCESS. YOU HAVE TO KEEP ON BEING FAITHFUL AND KEEP STEPPING UP. EVEN WHEN IT DOESN'T SEEM LIKE WHAT YOU'RE DOING REALLY MATTERS—TRUST ME, IT DOES. **"**

—DENNIS RAINEY

MAKING THE MOST OF YOUR TIME WITH YOUR KIDS[1]

A young professor once confided to a friend that one of his greatest struggles is getting fully engaged with his children when he is home. He has a hard time disengaging his mind from the projects he has at the office. Regardless of the occupation, many men find this to be one of the greatest challenges they face. Here are some tips to help you make the most of your time with your children.

Establish consistent, dedicated time with your kids. Jerry Jenkins, in his book *Hedges*, describes how he had no other agenda than connecting with his kids between the time he arrived home and their bedtime. During those hours, he did nothing for himself and focused on them.

Create accountability. If you are able to establish a regular routine like Mr. Jenkins, take it a step further by telling your children of your commitment. The accountability will do much to help you make the transition faster when you arrive home.

Eliminate distractions. Few things make your mind as scattered as trying to juggle all your digital devices while also engaging with your kids. Constantly checking the phone tells your kids that the distant people you are trying to connect with are more important than they are. Turn off your cell phone. Let it roll to voice mail. Turn off calendar alarms and text message alerts. This may not always be practical, but fight for it and let it become the norm. Also declare those hours to be computer and TV free. Eliminating electronic devices will force you to think creatively about ways to connect and give your kids good reasons to find ways to connect with you.

Be patient. With little kids, build extra time in your schedule for transitions. Trying to rush from one activity to another without lots of explaining creates frustration. A child's mind does not work as fast as yours, nor can they read your mind.

Know your world. Take your environment into account. For instance, the candy aisle at a grocery store can be pretty overwhelming to a four-year-old. You might be in and out, while they are just beginning to drool. When you are looking at a wall of snacks twice your height, you need time to ponder and reflect.

Meet eye-to-eye. When giving instruction, get down on their level and look into their eyes. Much parental frustration is rooted in either a child not hearing instruction or a parent giving a throwaway response in an effort to stop the barrage of questions. Remember that God made their little minds to ask, ask, ask, and learn, learn, learn.

Create shared experiences. Pick activities that they like, and learn with them. Also pick activities that you like, and be very intentional to teach your children at their level. If they don't get excited about it, try something else and be patient.

Share weekends. Most families let the weekend float up on them like an island of ocean trash, instead of making the most of the time they have. This often leads to frustration and boredom. Instead, plan your weekends in advance and build excitement for the event.

GOD CAN TURN YOUR HEART

Rob Rienow

Many a man desires to turn his heart to the ministry of his wife, yet some are stifled by the lack of a clear starting point. G. K. Chesterton said, "If a thing is worth doing, it is worth doing badly."[2] Meaning, it is better to do a little something than nothing at all.

If you've struggled to get started connecting with your wife spiritually, here are a few ideas to launch a life of productive spiritual leadership:

- Begin by praying for your own heart: "God, turn my heart to the ministry of my wife."

- Pray with your wife, even if it is only a few minutes a day.

- Try reading one Bible verse a day together. If time allows, discuss it as well.

- Consider taking a weekend away together to just discuss your vision and direction as a family.

- Attend a marriage conference (FamilyLife® offers a hotel-based Weekend to Remember® or The Art of Marriage® video event).

- Consider attending a couples' study at your church. If none is offered, then start one in your neighborhood. Both The Art of Marriage® small-group series and the Homebuilders Couples Series® are easy tools to use in leading a group discussion on marriage.

ARROWS

Like arrows in the hand of a warrior are the children of one's
youth. Blessed is the man who fills his quiver with them!

—Psalm 127:4–5a

STEPPING UP CREED

Every man has a creed to live by, a set of beliefs—though often unspoken—that guides his behavior. Some have it clearly defined, and for some it is deep inside. Today, we are calling you to step up to define and state your creed. As a man, you need to be clear about what guides and motivates you. What defines who you are? What makes you unique? What do you pound the table about? Why do you get out of bed every morning? What do you aspire to be? By the end of this day you will have answered these questions in the form of a Stepping Up Creed. (See page 77.)

Commit this creed to memory. Post it in prominent places. Review it regularly to remind yourself of God's specific call on your life. Share it with other men to gain their feedback and sharpening influence. Pray over it regularly to see if God has continued direction and tweaks to make along the way. And more importantly, make sure you are relying on the Word of God to shape everything you think, say, and do.

And let us consider how to stir up one another to love and good works.

–HEBREWS 10:24

Iron sharpens iron, and one man sharpens another.

–PROVERBS 27:17

God is teaching me life lessons that could help other men.

I need to step into the lives of other men.

Who has God placed in my life that I need to influence, help, or mentor?

Scan this code to learn about Stepping Up apps.

TAKE FIVE

One practical way you can step up is to call other men to step up with you by going through this material in a group. Many churches are using this event experience to launch the ten-week study. But we also want to challenge you to consider praying for God to open the doors for you to meet with a group of men who are not a part of your church.

Take a moment to brainstorm the names of five men to take through the ten-week study. It could include men at your workplace, men in your neighborhood, men who are long-time friends, or men that you golf/hunt/fish/bike/play ball with. Perhaps you and some friends will want to take your sons through the study together.

Write down the five names here:

1.

2.

3.

4.

5.

Look back over this list and see if one name jumps out who could help you organize the group. Circle that name and start by trying to talk to him this week.

Make the investment, take the step of faith, order a ten-week study, and start praying for men to be part of it. Find another man to pray with you about starting a group together. You can find out more about the study and review some of the material at MenSteppingUp.com.

We are praying that God will raise up a generation of equipped men who take steps of faith to engage other men about their convictions and faith. Whatever tools you choose to use, be one of those men.

THE STEPPING UP CREED

I will be a man who

I will display courage by *Pary*

I will pursue godliness by

I will make a difference by

I will step up and be the man God has called me to be.

NOTES

SESSION 1

1. "Edmund Hillary," Wikipedia, http://en.wikipedia.org/wiki/Edmund_Hillary.

2. "Mount Everest," Wikipedia, http://en.wikipedia.org/wiki/Mount_Everest.

3. Matt Rosenberg, "The World's Tallest Mountain – Mount Everest," http://geography.about.com/od/specificplacesofinterest/a/mounteverest.htm.

4. Ibid.

5. "Mount Everest," Wikipedia.

6. Mielikki Org, "Landing on Air," *National Geographic Adventure*, accessed October 3, 2012, http://www.nationalgeographic.com/adventure/0509/whats_new/helicopter_everest.html.

SESSION 2

1. "Statistical Reports: Firefighter Casualties," U.S. Fire Administration, FEMA, http://www.usfa.fema.gov/statistics/reports/firefighter_casualties.shtm.

2. "Firefighter Fatalities in 2000," U.S. Fire Administration Topical Fire Research Series, revised December 2001, http://www.usfa.fema.gov/downloads/pdf/statistics/v1i20-508.pdf.

3. Dennis Rainey, *Stepping Up: A Call to Courageous Manhood* (Little Rock, AR: FamilyLife Publishing, 2001), 137–142.

SESSION 3

1. Bronnie Ware, The Top Five Regrets Of The Dying: A Life Transformed by the Dearly Departing, (Carlsbad, CA: Hay House, 2012).

2. "Pornography Destroys Families," Partner Guard, accessed September 20, 2012, http://www.partner-guard.com/pornography/pornography-destroys-families.

3. Luke Gilkerson, "Just How Big is the Porn Business?" *Breaking Free Blog*, Covenant Eyes, April 29, 2008, http://www.covenanteyes.com/2008/04/29/just-how-big-is-the-porn-business.

4. Contributed by Bob Lepine. Used by permission.

SESSION 4

1. John C. Majors, "How to Get the Most out of Your Time with Your Kids," One Man Trying (blog), February 9, 2009, http://onemantrying.blogspot.com/2009/02/how-to-get-most-out-of-your-time-with.html. Used by permission.

2. G. K. Chesterton, *What's Wrong with the World* (New York: Dodd, Mead and Company, 1912), 320.

Voddie Baucham

Voddie Baucham Jr., DMin, is a husband, father, pastor, author, professor, conference speaker, and church planter. He currently serves as pastor of preaching at Grace Family Baptist Church in Spring, Texas. He and his wife, Bridget, have seven children.

Bill Bennett

William J. Bennett, PhD, is one of America's most influential voices on cultural, political, and educational issues. He is the host of a nationally broadcast radio show, *Bill Bennett's Morning in America*. Bill has written and edited sixteen books, two of which, *The Book of Virtues* and *The Children's Book of Virtues*, rank among the most successful of the past decade. He and his wife, Elayne, have two sons and live in Maryland.

Matt Chandler

Matt serves as lead pastor of The Village Church in Highland Village, Texas. He is also involved in church planting, both locally and internationally, through The Village and other partnerships. He is married to Lauren and they have three children.

Mark Driscoll

Mark is the founding pastor of Mars Hill Church in Seattle, Washington. He is one of the world's most downloaded and quoted pastors, with his audio sermon podcasts regularly being number one on iTunes for the Religion and Spirituality chart. He founded the Resurgence, which serves Christian leaders through books, blog posts, conferences, and classes. Mark and his wife, Grace, have five children.

Tony Dungy

Tony Dungy was born and raised in Jackson, Michigan. He and his wife, Lauren, have five children. Tony is a former professional football player and retired coach for the Indianapolis Colts. He became the first African-American coach to win a Super Bowl in 2007. In January 2009, Tony announced his retirement from the Colts, ending a thirty-one-year NFL career.

Matt Hammitt

Matt is a Christian singer-songwriter and a founding member of the band Sanctus Real. Over the past decade, the Grammy-nominated, Dove Award-winning group has released five albums and has topped the Christian radio charts with fourteen No. 1 and Top 5 radio hits. Matt and his wife, Sarah, have three children.

Joshua Harris

Joshua is the senior pastor of Covenant Life Church in Gaithersburg, Maryland. God has graciously allowed Joshua to write five books, including *I Kissed Dating Goodbye*, and his latest, *Dug Down Deep: Building Your Life on Truths That Last*. He and his wife, Shannon, have three children.

Robert Lewis

Robert Lewis, DMin, is the founder of Men's Fraternity. He is passionate about helping men discover the biblical principles of authentic manhood. He has authored a number of books, including *Raising a Modern-Day Knight* and *Rocking the Roles: Building a Win-Win Marriage*. Robert and his wife, Sherard, have four grown children.

Crawford Loritts

Crawford Loritts, DDiv, is the senior pastor of Fellowship Bible Church in Roswell, Georgia. He is the host of the daily radio program *Living a Legacy*, an internationally known Bible teacher, and an author of seven books. Crawford and his wife, Karen, are featured speakers at FamilyLife's marriage conferences. They have four grown children.

James MacDonald

James MacDonald, DMin, is the senior pastor of the Harvest Bible Chapel. His broadcast ministry *Walk in the Word* reaches more than three million people weekly. James's vision is that God will use him to plant 1,000 churches in his lifetime. He and his wife, Kathy, live in Illinois and have three grown children.

Dennis Rainey

Dennis is the president and CEO of FamilyLife, a ministry of Campus Crusade for Christ, and the co-host of the nationally syndicated *FamilyLife Today®* radio program. He has authored or coauthored more than two dozen books including *Stepping Up: A Call to Courageous Manhood*. Dennis has spoken at numerous Weekend to Remember® marriage getaways across the United States and internationally. Dennis and his wife, Barbara, have six children and nineteen grandchildren.

Rob Rienow

Rob married Amy in 1994 and they have been blessed with six children. He served as youth and family pastor at Wheaton Bible Church for eighteen years, and is now part of a church planting team in the Chicago area. God led Rob and Amy to launch Visionary Family Ministries, a ministry to inspire parents and grandparents to disciple their children, help couples create mission-driven marriages, and equip churches to build Bible-driven ministries. Their mission is to build the church through a global reformation of family discipleship.

Stu Weber

Stu served as a Green Beret in Vietnam. It was there that he committed himself to a lifetime of vocational ministry. He and his wife, Linda, later joined a small group of friends in founding Good Shepherd Community Church near Portland, Oregon. Stu is much in demand as an international speaker, and he is the author of several books, including *Tender Warrior, Four Pillars of a Man's Heart, All the King's Men,* and *Along the Road to Manhood.*

Tim Grissom

Tim is a writer living in Little Rock, Arkansas, where he also serves as senior editor for FamilyLife Publishing. He is the author of numerous articles, has contributed to several books, and is the coauthor of the best-selling book, *Seeking Him.* Tim loves to help people understand how deeply the Bible speaks to the issues of life and to encourage them to find their rest in God.

John Majors

John has served with FamilyLife since 2000. He has helped create key resources like The Art of Marriage and Passport2Purity. His passion is to equip men with resources for teaching their families the Bible. He and his wife, Julie, have two children.

Enjoy the Stepping Up Video Event?
IDEAS FOR A NEXT STEP

FOR YOURSELF

- Read *Stepping Up™: A Call to Courageous Manhood*.

- Join an accountability group or seek out a mentor who models biblical manhood.

- Listen to *FamilyLife Today®* **radio broadcast**—daily encouragement from a biblical perspective.

- Seek help with a personal issue by contacting an eMentor confidentially at www.FamilyLife.com/eMentoring .

WITH OTHER GUYS

- Build into the lives of other men through a group study of the **Stepping Up™ video series**.

WITH YOUR WIFE

- Connect with your spouse at a **Weekend to Remember® marriage getaway**. Find dates and locations at WeekendtoRemember.com.

AT YOUR CHURCH

- Host **The Art of Marriage® video event**. Discover God's design for marriage at this one and a half day event.

- Lead a group study of a marriage or parenting issue using the **Homebuilders Couples Series®**, the **Homebuilders Parenting Series®**, or **Marriage Oneness video series**.

- Build into the lives of other men or make marriages and families stronger. Contact our Coaching Team for a no commitment, free consultation on how to get started.

> Visit FamilyLife.com/HomeBuilder
> Call 1-800-FL-TODAY
> E-mail HBcoaching@FamilyLife.com

Learn more about these and many other ministry tools at FamilyLife.com

MEN, IT'S TIME TO STEP UP.
DON'T GO IT ALONE.

Today was just a start. There's more for you to learn and do as a man.

We're pleased to offer the 10-week Stepping Up video series, an opportunity for you and a group of friends to continue the journey together. In addition to what you experienced through the one-day event, the video series will guide your group into a greater understanding of the challenges and rewards of biblical manhood. Using video, personal devotional exercises, and group interaction, each man will

- examine key Bible passages related to courage and faith,
- identify the issues that tend to erode his courage,
- solicit an evaluation of his life from men he knows and respects,
- get help for strengthening relationships and rebuilding broken ones,
- develop a personalized Stepping Up Plan, and
- much more!

The 10-week video series kit includes

- leader's guide
- workbook
- three DVDs featuring ten 25–35 minute video sessions
- *Stepping Up* book

Learn more, view product samples, and place orders at MenSteppingUp.com

ABOUT FAMILYLIFE®

FamilyLife is a donor-supported nonprofit organization headquartered in Little Rock, Arkansas, whose mission is to develop godly marriages and families whochange the world one home at a time. While our culture says it's just part of life when families become disconnected or split, we say it doesn't have to be that way.

Helping You Help Others

God is looking for HomeBuilders, people who are passionate about building godly marriages and families, to bring hope back to homes. Are you willing to be a HomeBuilder, and step out of your comfort zone and do something that will impact lives forever?

We stand ready to help you as a HomeBuilder to minister to and through others, so you can have the greatest impact in your church and community. Our desire is to support you and the church with tools based on biblical truths about how God designed marriage and family relationships. We also seek to provide you with resources that require minimal preparation, so you can be empowered to reach more people for Christ.

Visit **FamilyLife.com** today to find the tools and resources you need to get started impacting the marriages and families around you.